Laundry Day

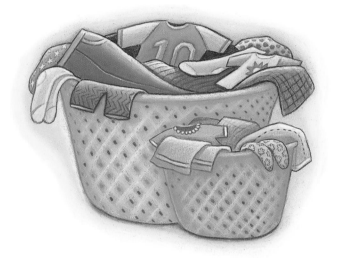

written by Karen Hjemboe

illustrated by Shelly Hehen

Bebop Books

An imprint of LEE & LOW BOOKS Inc.

In go the socks.

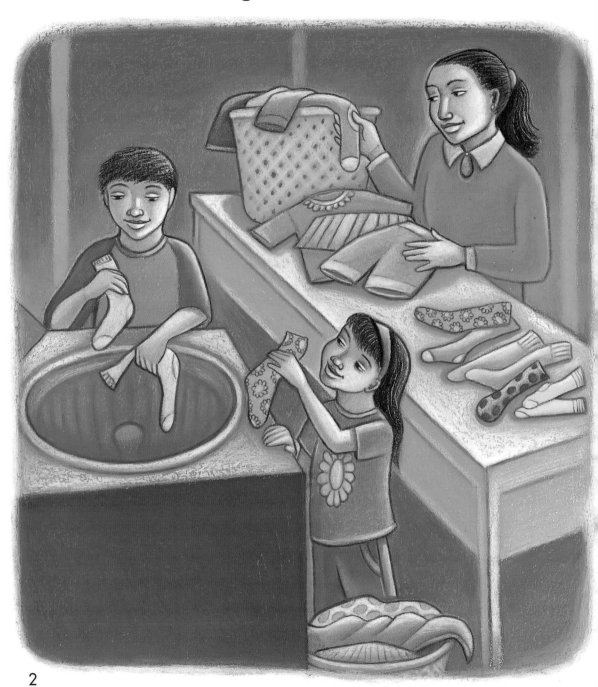

In go the pants.

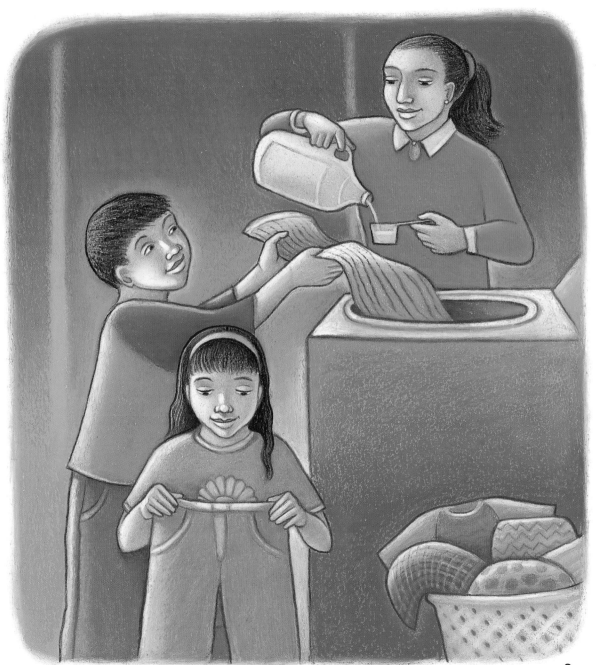

In go the shirts.

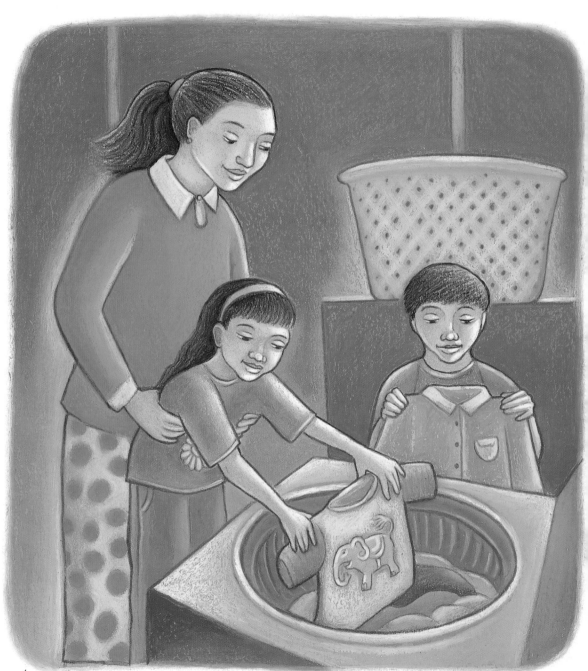

Out come the socks.

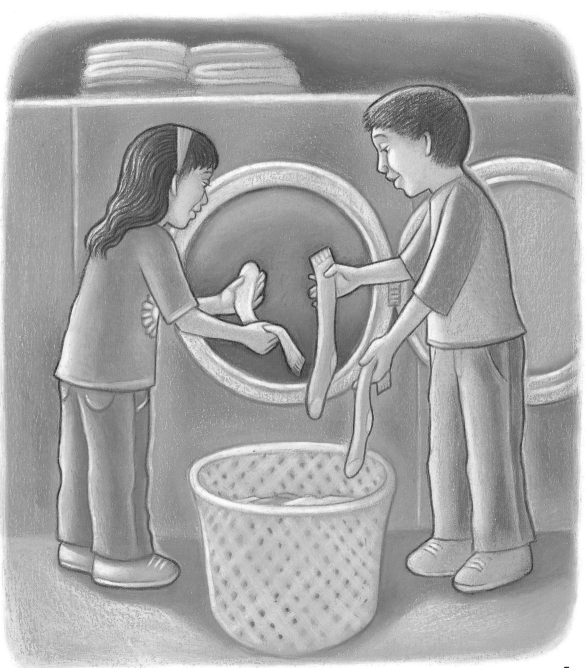

Out come the pants.

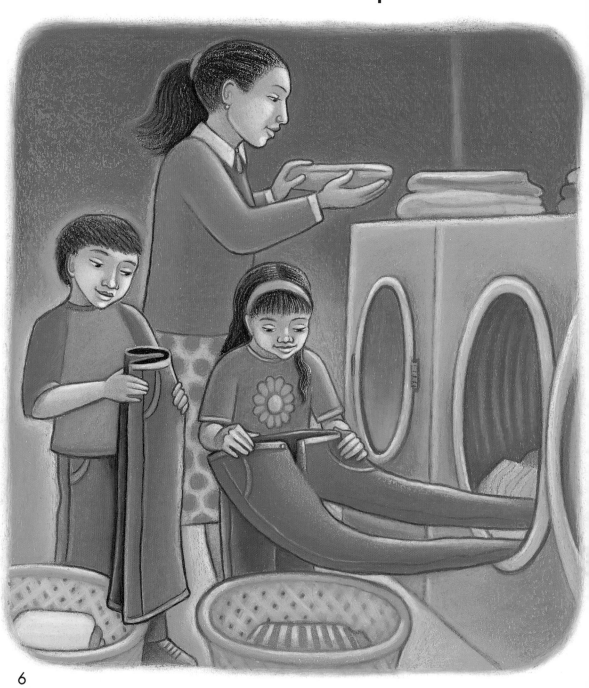

Out come the shirts.

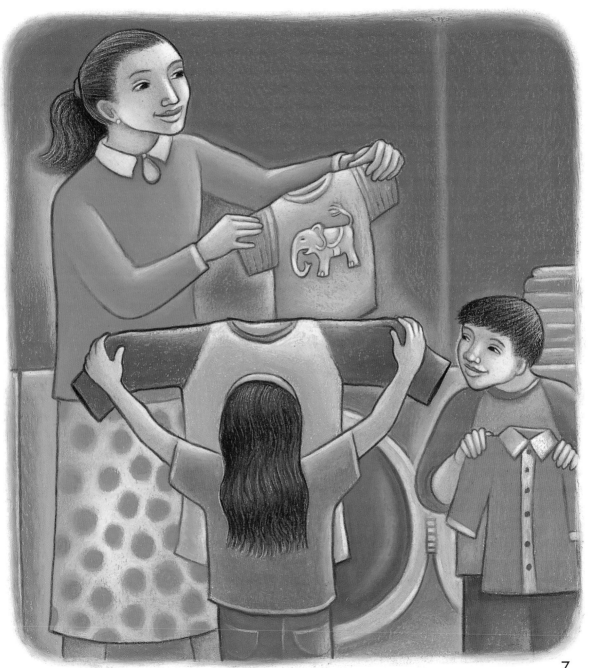

Out come the people.

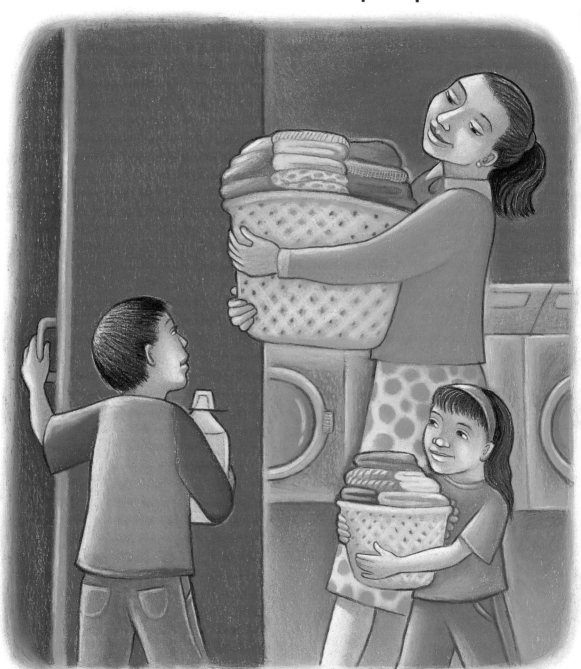